ULTIMATE PIRATE STICKER FILE

Have fun completing the pirate sticker and colouring activities! Pull out the sticker sheets and keep them by you when you complete each sticker activity page. There are also extra stickers to use throughout this book or anywhere you want!

make believe ideas

Sea Eggs!

Draw funny faces on the eggs.

Find the missing sea eggs.

Colour the captain's dragon bright green!

Sticker more yellow spots.

Ahoy There!

Use stickers to
decorate the
ship's sails!

Colour
the
pirate
ship.

8

PIRATE FACES

Use your stickers to give
the pirates funny faces.

Cook up a Storm!

Doodle a yummy plate of food for the pirates.
Don't forget to use your stickers!

Sticker the missing creepy-crawlies.

Draw silly faces on the pile of peas!

CANNON CATASTROPHE!

Draw faces on the fruits and vegetables flying out of the cannons.

Find 3 more cannonballs!

PIRATE PATTERNS

Complete the patterns by finding the missing stickers.

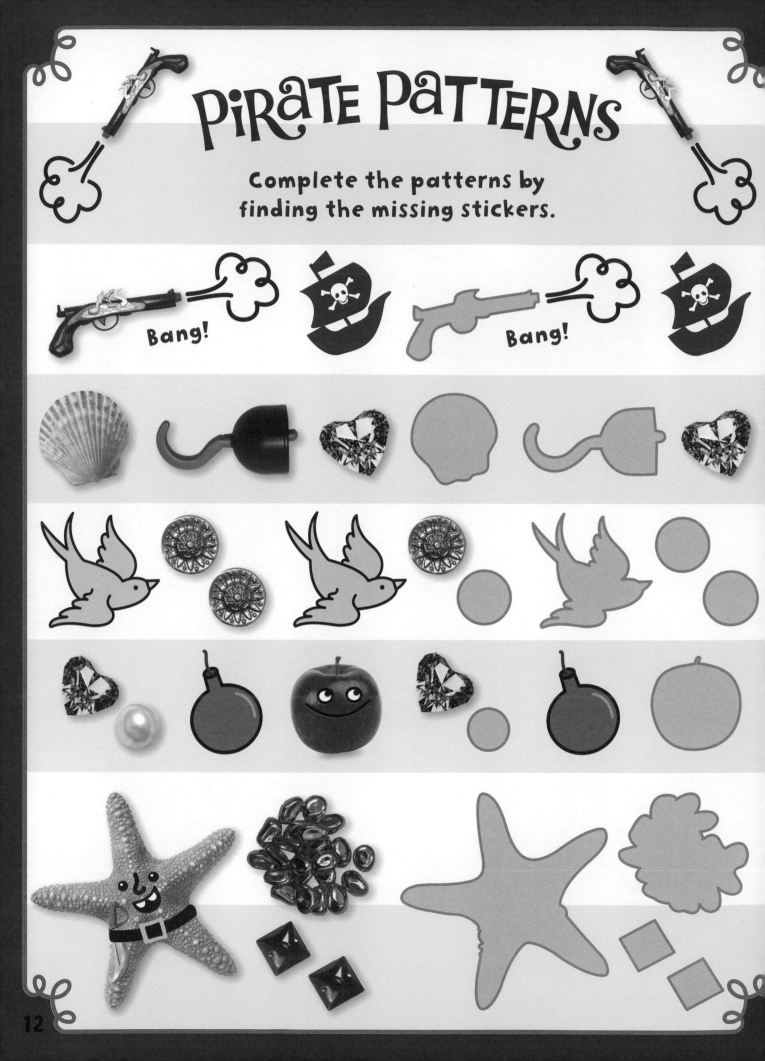

SHiVER, ME TiMBERS!

Draw a pirate ship in the bottle!

LOOK OUT, MATEY!

Sticker the missing pieces to complete the puzzle.

Can you find the missing treasure?

DRESS LikE a PiRate!

Design your own pirate hat!

Sticker and colour the pirate accessories.

PiRate PARtY!

Use stickers and colour
to finish the party scene.

DINNERTIME

Colour Penny Pirate's kitchen!

Sticker the missing food.

Count the sizzling sausages!

Pirates love sausages!

18

GhoST ShiP!

Find and sticker the skeletons.

How many skeletons can you count? 19

LAND ahoy!

Bang!

Argh!

Colour the pirates.

Watch out for sharks!

Avast!

How many pirates can you count?

....

21

Sail The Seven Seas!

Sticker the missing pieces
to complete the puzzle.

Can you find the missing fish?

IT'S A PIRATE'S LIFE FOR, ME!

Colour the pirate in peril and the snapping shark.

Walk the plank, ye old scallywag!

Help the pirates finish their sums by finding the missing answers.

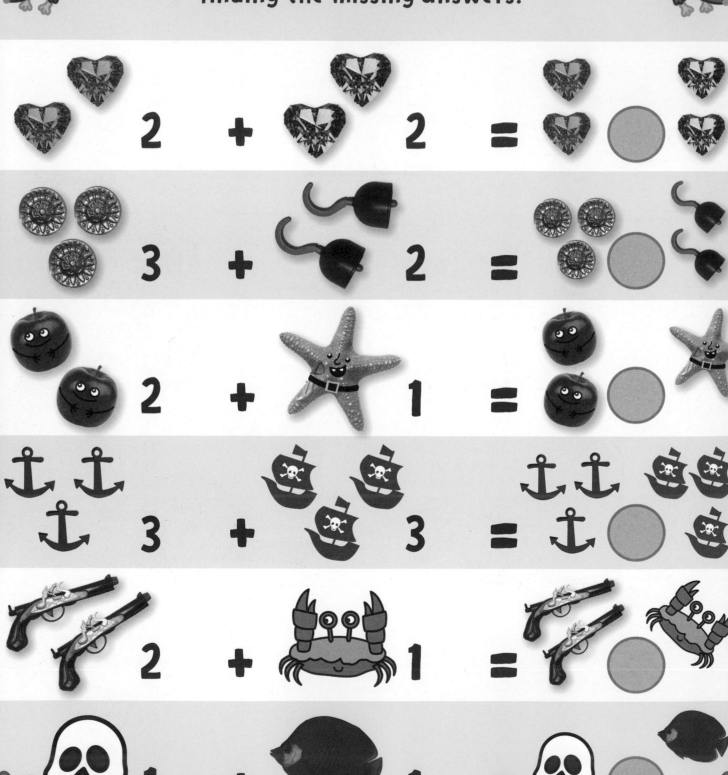

2 + 2 =

3 + 2 =

2 + 1 =

3 + 3 =

2 + 1 =

1 + 1 =

The Big Blue Sea!

Sticker and colour the underwater creatures.

What teatime treats are caught on the line?

How many coins can you find?

....

COOL TREASURE

Find the missing stickers and make the treasure colourful.

YO-HO-HO!

Draw tattoos on the pirates' arms.

Use the grid to copy the ship's wheel.

27

MAROONED MATES!

Draw a pirate ship to rescue the pirates.

Find the missing treasure.

PIRATE FISHING!

Design a pirate flag.

Sticker what the pirates have caught.

Colour the anchor.

SLEEPY PIRATES

Shhh! Don't wake the pirates.
Find the missing stickers.

CRAZY CROCODILE!

Use colour to decorate the ship.

Find the pirate's T-shirt.

...ake me bright green!

Snap!

31

UNDERWATER CREATURES

Follow the trails to find out
which crab lives under each shell.

COLOURFUL COINS!

Colour the pirate coins.

Draw a pirate face in the coin.

Use your stickers to add more coins.

JOLLY ROGERS!

Design your own pirate flags with stickers and colour.

PiRate PoRtRaits

Doodle pirate faces in the picture frames.

Give the pirate a red beard!

WHAT CAN YOU SEE THROUGH THE PIRATE'S TELESCOPE?

Sticker more treasure!

PIRATE PLAYTIME!

Decorate the pirate ship using your stickers.

How many coins can you count?

○ ....

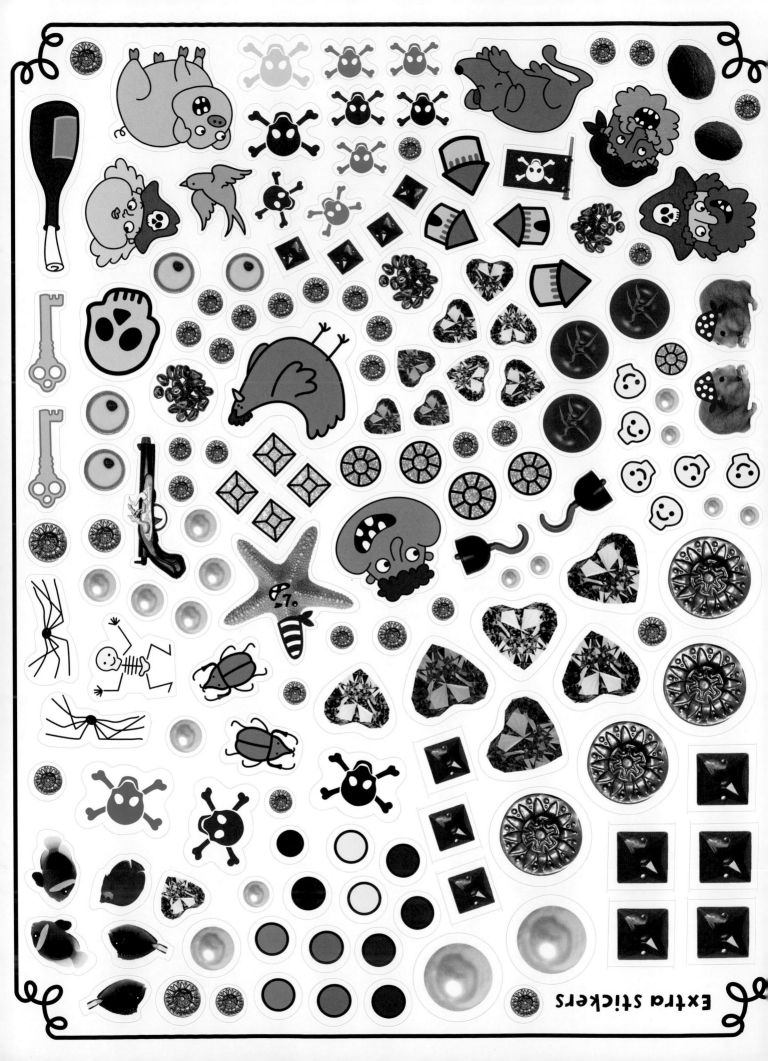

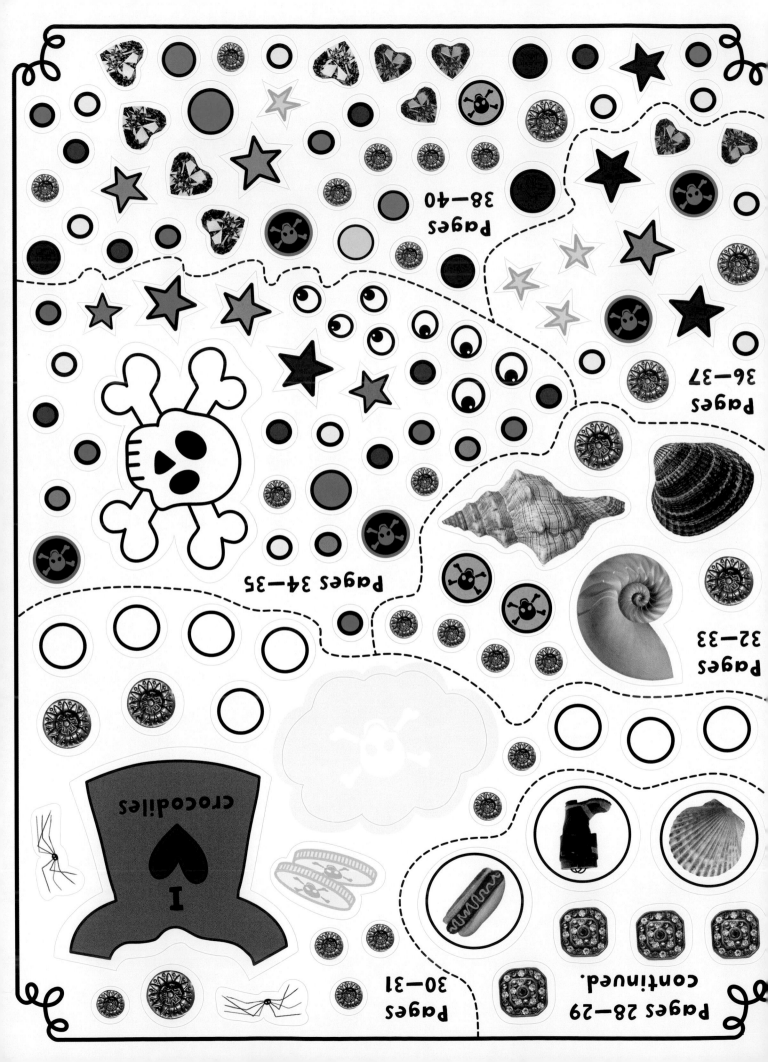

Pages 38–40

Pages 36–37

Pages 34–35

Pages 32–33

Pages 30–31

Pages 28–29 continued.

crocodiles

Pages 26–27

Pages 28–29

Pages 24–25

Pages 22–23

Pages 20–21

Pages 16–17

Pages 18–19

Pages 14–15

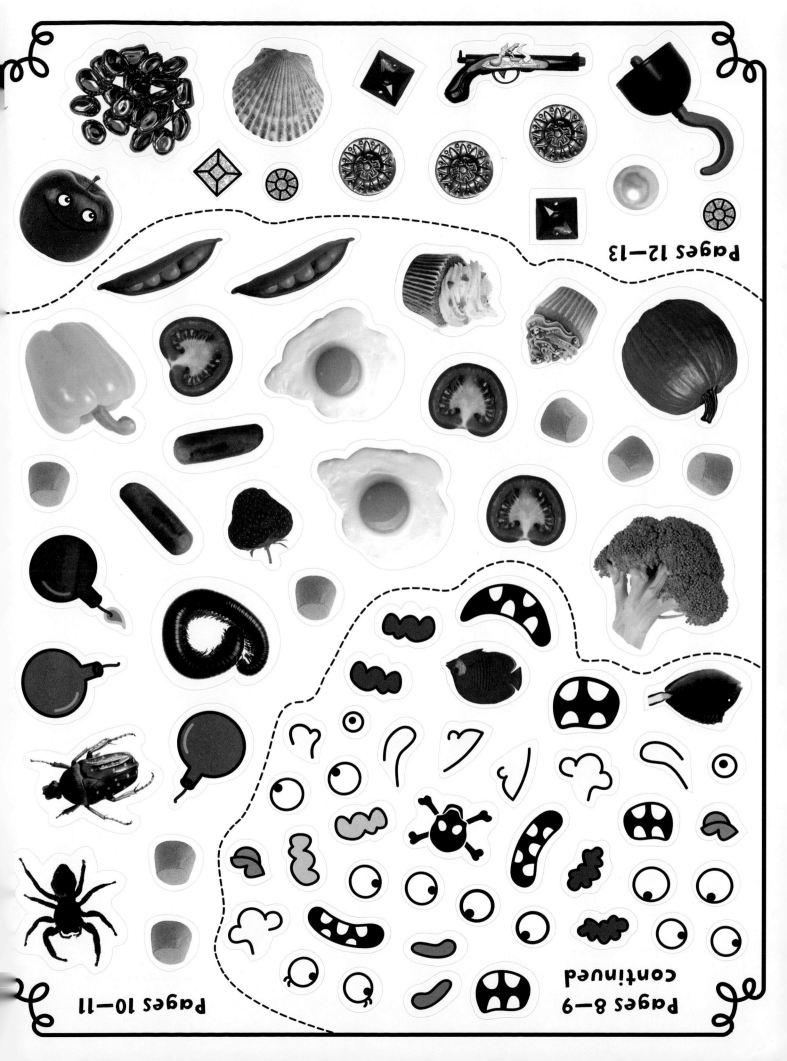

Pages 10-11

Pages 8-9 continued

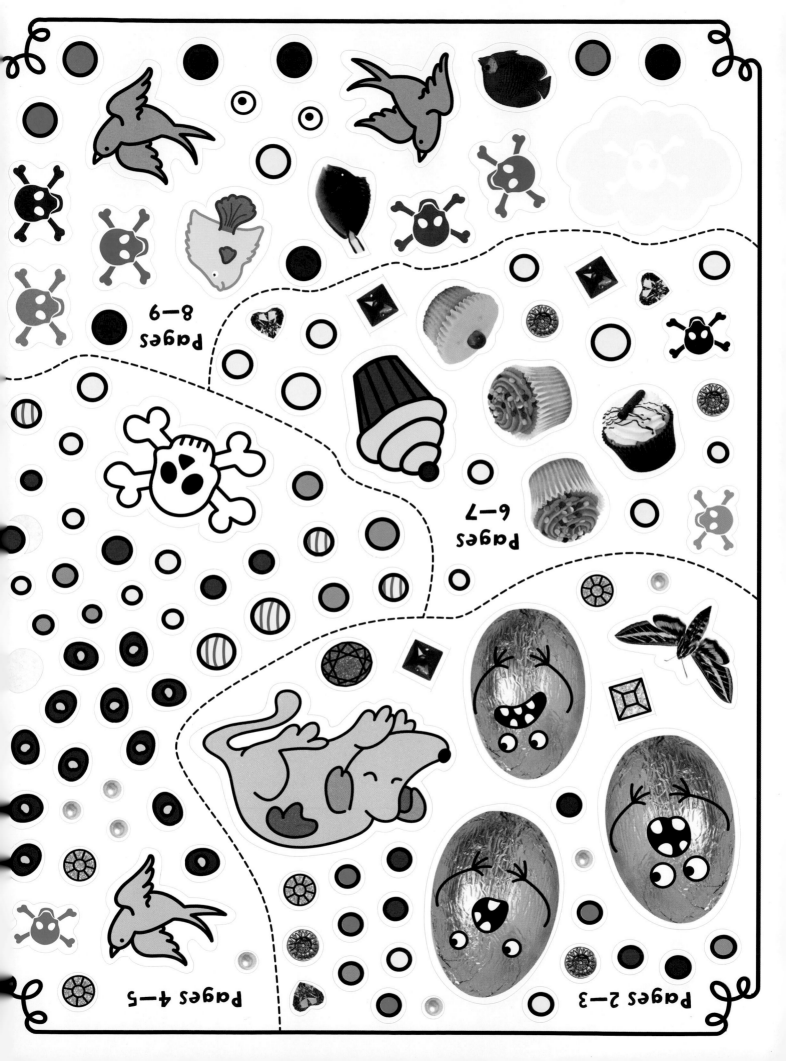

Pages 8—9

Pages 6—7

Pages 4—5

Pages 2—3